Crabby Crab lives in Green Creek.
Today the sky is very gray.
Crabby feels a drop of rain.
This makes Crabby feel crabby.

1

Crabby sees Freddie Fish in the creek.
"Good day, friend," Freddie says.
"Why are you so grouchy?"

"The sky is gray," Crabby groans.

2

Crabby sees Fran Frog on a log.
"Hello, friend," Fran croaks.
"Why are you so grumpy?"

"It is not a pretty day," Crabby grunts.

3

Crabby sees Grub Bug in the grass.
"Hi, friend," Grub says.
"Why are you so cross?"

"It is not sunny," Crabby grumbles.

 4

Crabby sees Brady Beaver by a tree.
"Hey, friend," Brady says.
"Why are you so dreary?"

"I feel drops of rain," Crabby cries.

Crabby sees Trish Turtle on the trail.
Trish has a basket of bread.
"Greetings, friend," Trish says.
"Would you like some bread?"

6

Drip, drop, drip, drop!
Trish and Crabby crawl under a tree.
Crabby grumbles about the rain.
Trish says, "I like the rain with a friend."

Trish and Crabby eat bread together.
Crabby grins at Trish.
Crabby is not crabby anymore.
Crabby says, "This is a great day!"